THE AUTHORITY
THE MAGNIFICENT

Writer: **Garth Ennis**   Artist: **Carlos Ezquerra**

Colors: **David Baron**   Letters: **Phil Balsman**

Covers: **Glenn Fabry**   Design: **Larry Berry**

Special thanks: **Tony Luke & Alan Passalaqua**   THE AUTHORITY created by **Warren Ellis and Bryan Hitch**

For Keith, #1 Kev fan

THE AUTHORITY: THE MAGNIFICENT KEVIN published by WildStorm Productions. 888 Prospect St. #240, La Jolla, CA 92037. Compilation © 2006 WildStorm Productions, an imprint of DC Comics. All Rights Reserved. Wildstorm Universe Series and its logo, The Authority, all characters, the distinctive likenesses thereof and all related elements are trademarks of DC Comics. Originally published in single magazine form as THE AUTHORITY: THE MAGNIFICENT KEVIN © 2005, 2006 DC Comics.

DC Comics, a Warner Bros. Entertainment Company.

ISBN: 1-4012-0990-4   ISBN-13: 978-1-4012-0990-2

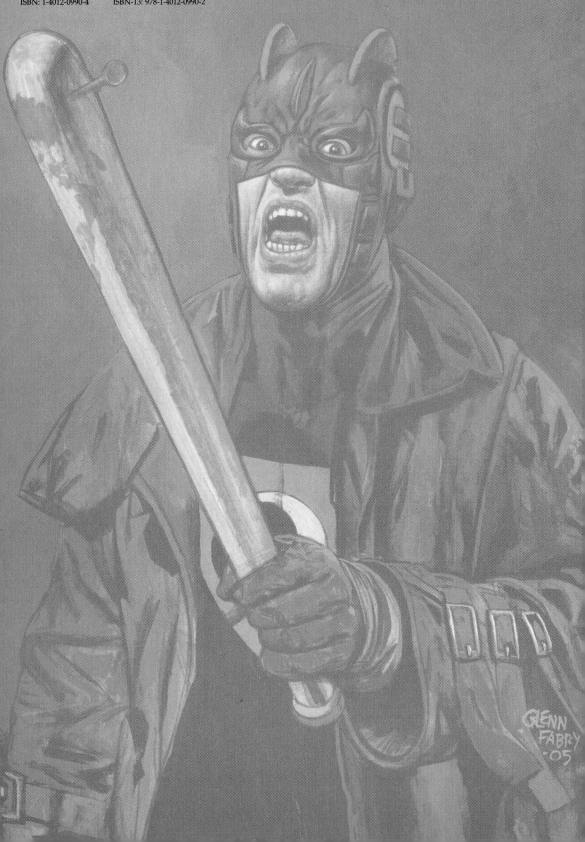

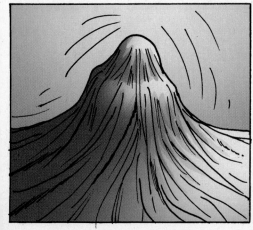

THE CARRIER

♫ DAH-NAH-NAH-NAHHH, DAH-NAH-NA NAHHH...WUKKA-WUKKA-WUKKA-WUKKA ♫
(PORNO MUSIC)

OH, FUCKING WONDERFUL...

I SEE THE LOVE THAT DARE NOT NEIGH ITS NAME HAS ONCE MORE RETURNED TO HAUNT US.

MM. AND THE REST.

All the Pretty Horsecocks

ALTHOUGH COME TO THINK OF IT, THE DOCTOR SHOOTING SMACK AND WATCHING GIRLS BLOWING HORSES IS ONE OF THE FEW SIGNS OF NORMALITY LEFT AROUND HERE...

IT WAS JUST A SUGGESTION, MIDNIGHTER. I MEAN WE WERE AT A GROUP MEETING, EVERYONE WAS FREE TO SAY WHATEVER THEY WANTED.

I DON'T GIVE TWO TUGS OF A DEAD POODLE'S COCK. WE ARE NOT FUCKING GETTING DECODER RINGS.

BUT...

THERE IS NO BUT. THERE IS NO DEBATE HERE OF ANY KIND.

SIGNATURE REQUIRED, MATEY!

FUCK OFF A MINUTE, FROGGETT. I'M TRYING TO HEAR THIS.

...AND AS THEY COME INTO THE HOME STRAIT IT'S *VIRGIN MEGASTORE!* VIRGIN MEGASTORE PASSING HELEN'S AWFUL UNCLE!

PASSING *DIESEL NOT UNLEADED!* PASSING TEN PEE MIX-UP! NOTHING CAN POSSIBLY STOP THE *THIRTY TO ONE OUTSIDER* NOW, AND--

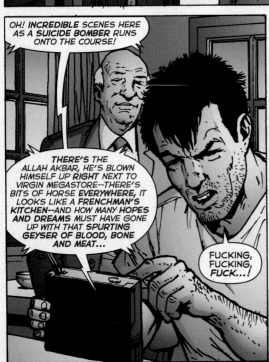

OH! *INCREDIBLE* SCENES HERE AS A *SUICIDE BOMBER* RUNS ONTO THE COURSE!

THERE'S THE *ALLAH AKBAR,* HE'S BLOWN HIMSELF UP *RIGHT* NEXT TO VIRGIN MEGASTORE--THERE'S BITS OF HORSE EVERYWHERE, IT LOOKS LIKE A *FRENCHMAN'S KITCHEN*--AND HOW MANY *HOPES* AND *DREAMS* MUST HAVE GONE UP WITH THAT *SPURTING GEYSER* OF BLOOD, BONE AND MEAT...

FUCKING, FUCKING, *FUCK...!*

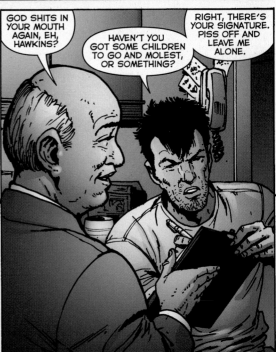

GOD SHITS IN YOUR MOUTH AGAIN, EH, HAWKINS?

HAVEN'T YOU GOT SOME CHILDREN TO GO AND MOLEST, OR SOMETHING?

RIGHT, THERE'S YOUR SIGNATURE. PISS OFF AND LEAVE ME ALONE.

MY PLEASURE. TELL YOU WHAT, NEXT TIME THE BOGTROTTERS CATCH UP WITH YOU I'LL LEAVE YOU TO CLEAN UP THE MESS YOURSELF, SHALL I?

YOU WOULDN'T LIKE THAT, WOULD YOU, MATEY? NO, NO, MATEY WOULDN'T LIKE THAT AT ALL...

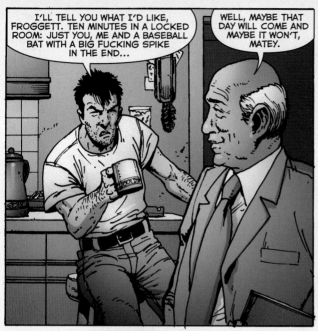

I'LL TELL YOU WHAT I'D LIKE, FROGGETT. TEN MINUTES IN A LOCKED ROOM: JUST YOU, ME AND A BASEBALL BAT WITH A BIG FUCKING SPIKE IN THE END...

WELL, MAYBE THAT DAY WILL COME AND MAYBE IT WON'T, MATEY.

BUT IF IT DOES, MAYBE I WON'T BE THE PUSHOVER YOU THINK I AM.

MAYBE THE BIG, TOUGH HERO FROM THE REGIMENT WILL BITE OFF MORE THAN HE CAN CHEW.

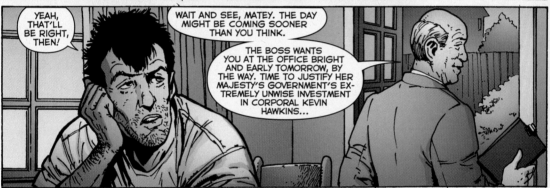

YEAH, THAT'LL BE RIGHT, THEN!

WAIT AND SEE, MATEY. THE DAY MIGHT BE COMING SOONER THAN YOU THINK.

THE BOSS WANTS YOU AT THE OFFICE BRIGHT AND EARLY TOMORROW, BY THE WAY. TIME TO JUSTIFY HER MAJESTY'S GOVERNMENT'S EX-TREMELY UNWISE INVESTMENT IN CORPORAL KEVIN HAWKINS...

CUNT.

HELLO?

KEV? MICK. BAD NEWS, MATE.

MICK, BELIEVE ME: AT THIS POINT THERE IS NO FUCKING WAY THAT MY DAY CAN GET ANY WORSE...

I WOULDN'T BE TOO SURE ABOUT THAT. TINY JUST SHOT HIMSELF.

WHAT?

HE WAS HOME FOR THE WEEKEND.

HIS DAD FOUND HIM.

AW, FUCK.

WE HAD A PINT WITH HIM JUST THE OTHER NIGHT, HE SEEMED ALL RIGHT THEN...

POOR OLD TINY. I WONDER WHAT HE WAS THINKING.

MIGHT HAVE BEEN BOSNIA. YOU REMEMBER THAT THING, WHERE TINY CALLED IN THE AIRSTRIKE BUT THE YANKS DIDN'T WANT TO RISK A PLANE?

IT WAS JUST HIM ON HIS OWN, HE HAD TO SIT AND WATCH THE SERBS STEAM INTO TOWN AND KILL ABOUT A HUNDRED WOMEN AND KIDS...

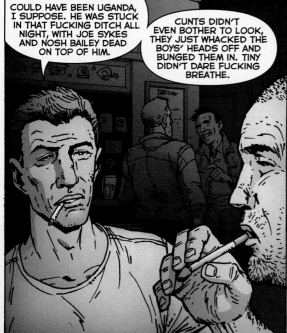

COULD HAVE BEEN UGANDA, I SUPPOSE. HE WAS STUCK IN THAT FUCKING DITCH ALL NIGHT, WITH JOE SYKES AND NOSH BAILEY DEAD ON TOP OF HIM.

CUNTS DIDN'T EVEN BOTHER TO LOOK, THEY JUST WHACKED THE BOYS' HEADS OFF AND BUNGED THEM IN. TINY DIDN'T DARE FUCKING BREATHE.

OR IRAQ, IN NINETY-ONE. FUCKING JUNDIES HAD HIM FOR WEEKS, THEY TORTURED HIM EVERY BLOODY DAY OF IT.

FUCK, IT WAS PROBABLY ALL THE SHIT THAT TINY AND THE REST OF US PUT UP WITH.

YOU THINK IT'S ONLY A JOB?

I THINK THIS WHOLE THING REMINDS ME OF DANNY.

I DUNNO IF I SHOULD TELL YOU THIS, BUT THERE'S A BIT MORE TO HIM LEGGING IT THAN EVERYONE THINKS...

DON'T WORRY ABOUT IT, MATE. I ALWAYS THOUGHT IT WAS A BIT DODGY, HIM SNEAKING A MAN-EATING TIGER PAST YOU.

"YEAH, WELL, IT WASN'T JUST THE TIGER."

"IT WAS THE JOB, REALLY. HE SAID HE'D LOOKED AT IT FROM EVERY ANGLE AND HE COULDN'T SEE ONE SINGLE THING GOOD ABOUT IT. HE WAS WORRIED THAT ONE DAY HE'D GET ORDERED TO DO SOMETHING REALLY OUTRAGEOUS, SLOTTING CIVVIES OR KIDS OR WHATEVER.

"THAT'S WHY HE DID A RUNNER."

NOW IT CAN BE TOLD.

I DUNNO, KEV. YOU KNOW WHY I QUIT? MORE THAN ANYTHING ELSE, REALLY?

IT WAS BECAUSE NO MATTER HOW HARD I TRIED, I JUST COULDN'T THINK LIKE OLD MICK OVER THERE.

AND I SUPPOSE, IN THE END...

NEITHER COULD OUR MATE TINY.

IT GOT HAWKSMOOR WHEN HE WAS ON THE COMMODE. OBVIOUSLY THE DOCTOR WAS IN NO SHAPE TO DEFEND HIMSELF.

ENGINEER, WHAT THE HELL *IS IT?*

I HAVEN'T EVEN SEEN IT, WHATEVER IT IS. I SUPPOSE WE OUGHT TO START WITH THESE... PIES...

IT'S LIGHTNING-FAST, I CAN TELL YOU THAT MUCH. SEEMS TO RELY ON SOME KIND OF TELE-PORTATION.

ALL RIGHT, THE PIES: YOU WANT TO TRY TAKING ONE OF THEM OFF?

WAIT A MINUTE, WE'RE ASSUMING IT'S FEEDING HIM OXYGEN. IF WE TAKE IT OFF--WE COULD KILL HIM.

WELL, IT'S ONLY THE DOCTOR.

YOU'LL TAKE THE RESPONSIBILITY?

HAPPY TO.

YOU'RE TEARING THE SKIN...

I KNOW...

I'M

HAWKINS?

HAWKINS...

MMM?

HAVE YOU BEEN LISTENING TO A SINGLE WORD I'VE SAID?

OH, SORRY, BOSS...

PAY ATTENTION, FOR GOD'S SAKE. I'VE BETTER THINGS TO DO WITH MY TIME THAN SPEND IT WITH THE LIKES OF YOU.

AS I WAS SAYING, M.I.5 RECEIVED A COMMUNICATION LATE LAST NIGHT FROM A RATHER UNEXPECTED SOURCE. YOUR OLD FRIEND THE MIDNIGHTER, TO BE PRECISE.

IT SEEMS THE AUTHORITY HAVE RUN INTO A SPOT OF TROUBLE...

OH, NOT THAT SHOWER OF CUNTS AGAIN!

EVERY FUCKING TIME THEY SHOW UP I END UP STUCK IN THE SHIT! AND THE MIDNIGHTER AND WHATSIZNAME, APOLLO-- THE PANZER COMMANDER AND THE MILKMAID, MORE LIKE! THOSE TWO POOFS ARE THE WORST OF THE LOT!

HE'S NOT GONNA REST TILL HE'S SLIT MY THROAT, D'YOU KNOW THAT? THE MIDNIGHTER? THE CUNT CAN'T TAKE A JOKE, HE THINKS THAT JUST BECAUSE YOU ACCIDENTALLY BLOW SOMEONE'S HEAD OFF--

WELL, THAT IS ODD. HE SAYS YOU'RE THE ONLY ONE HE TRUSTS TO BRING HIM IN.

...YOU FUCKING *WHAT?*

THE CARRIER CAME UNDER ATTACK LAST NIGHT, WE'RE NOT EXACTLY SURE BY WHOM. THE MIDNIGHTER WAS THE ONLY ONE TO ESCAPE--HE MAY EVEN BE THE SOLE SURVIVOR.

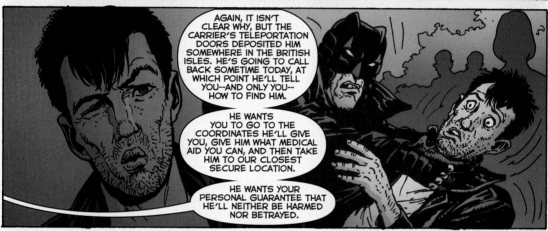

AGAIN, IT ISN'T CLEAR WHY, BUT THE CARRIER'S TELEPORTATION DOORS DEPOSITED HIM SOMEWHERE IN THE BRITISH ISLES. HE'S GOING TO CALL BACK SOMETIME TODAY, AT WHICH POINT HE'LL TELL YOU--AND ONLY YOU-- HOW TO FIND HIM.

HE WANTS YOU TO GO TO THE COORDINATES HE'LL GIVE YOU, GIVE HIM WHAT MEDICAL AID YOU CAN, AND THEN TAKE HIM TO OUR CLOSEST SECURE LOCATION.

HE WANTS YOUR PERSONAL GUARANTEE THAT HE'LL NEITHER BE HARMED NOR BETRAYED.

BOSS, THIS BLOKE *FUCKING HATES ME...*

BUT FOR SOME REASON HE TRUSTS YOU. AND GIVEN THIS AGENCY'S HISTORY WITH APOLLO AND THE MIDNIGHTER, WE'VE DECIDED TO EXTEND HIM EVERY ASSISTANCE.

YEAH?

WHAT HISTORY, EXACTLY? HOW IS IT YOU KNOW THOSE TWO SO WELL?

WHY DOES AN *ANARCHIST SUPERHERO* COME LOOKING FOR HELP FROM A BIRD AT BRITISH INTELLIGENCE...?

BIRD...?

WOMAN.

THE ANSWER IS: NONE OF YOUR BUSINESS.

YOURS IS NEVER TO REASON WHY, HAWKINS. YOURS IS SIMPLY TO FOLLOW EVERY ORDER YOU'RE GIVEN TO THE LETTER.

SO THE SAME OLD BOLLOCKS AS USUAL, THEN.

I BEG YOUR PARDON, DO YOU HAVE A COMPLAINT YOU'D LIKE TO LODGE?

YOU, DON'T FORGET, ARE THE IDIOT WHO GOT A GOVERNMENT OFFICIAL DEVOURED BY A TIGER, AND AS SUCH YOU WILL CONTINUE TO DRAW EVERY WRETCHED ASSIGNMENT GOING UNTIL GOD FINALLY CORRECTS HIS MISTAKE AND DOES AWAY WITH YOU. AND SHOULD YOU FIND YOURSELF UNABLE TO BEAR THIS BURDEN, AND BECOME--SAY-- HABITUALLY INSUBORDINATE TO A SUPERIOR, YOU WILL FIND THAT GOD WILL BE GIVEN A *HELPING HAND...*

AND I WILL HAVE YOU STRUNG FROM WATERLOO BRIDGE BY YOUR FORESKIN.

MM...COURSE, YOU DO NEED ME TO GO AND FETCH THE MIDNIGHTER, DON'T YOU?

TRUE...

SO YOU CAN'T REALLY SLOT ME FOR LIP TILL THE JOB'S OVER, CAN YOU?

ALSO TRUE...

SO.

I DON'T SUPPOSE THERE'S ANY CHANCE OF A BLOW-JOB?

Next: *The Kevin Samurai*

CHRIST ALL-BLOODY-MIGHTY.

WHAT THE FUCK'S HE DOING UP HERE?

HELLO? *MIDNIGHTER?*

IT'S KEV HAWKINS! I'M HERE! I'M ON MY OWN, JUST LIKE I SAID ON THE PHONE!

WELL?

LOOK, ARE YOU HERE OR WHAT?

MIDNIGHTER?

FUCKING POOF PROBABLY TOLD ME THE WRONG CAVE...

FUCKING CUNT, YOU NEARLY GAVE ME A HEART ATTACK!

I *LOOKED* THERE...!

THE OUTFIT ABSORBS LIGHT. ALL I HAD TO DO WAS HOLD MY BREATH.

VERY FUCKING FUN-- JESUS, WHAT THE HELL HAPPENED TO YOU?

...I'M A VAGINA? THAT'S ALL IT SAID?

THAT'S ALL.

I OPENED A DOOR JUST BEFORE THE AIRLOCK PURGED. WHY IT TOOK ME TO THE ENGLISH PEAK DISTRICT I HAVE NO IDEA; THE WHOLE SYSTEM NOW SEEMS TO BE DOWN.

WHAT'S ALSO STRANGE IS THAT MY WOUNDS AREN'T HEALING. BY NOW I OUGHT TO BE ALMOST AS GOOD AS NEW, BUT...

YOU'RE A--FAT FUCKING BASTARD, I'LL-- FUCKING TELL YOU THAT MUCH--

I'LL ASK SWIFT HOW SHE KEEPS HER FIGURE. SPEAKING OF PURGING.

THE POINT IS I'M COMPLETELY USELESS IN THIS CONDITION; I'VE GOT NOTHING BUT ONE GOOD ARM, A CELLPHONE AND MY DICK. THAT'S WHY I'VE ASKED BRITISH INTELLIGENCE FOR HELP.

BUT WHY--

ME?

NEEDS MUST WHEN THE DEVIL DRIVES, HAWKINS.

EH? WHAT'S THAT SUPPOSED TO MEAN?

APOLLO AND THE OTHERS ARE IN TROUBLE. I HAD NO CHOICE.

WHICH LEAVES ME AT THE MERCY OF YOUR BOSS--WHO I'VE NEVER BEEN TOO SURE ABOUT--AND YOU: A HOMOPHOBIC LOSER WITH A TALENT FOR SCREWING UP SPECTACULARLY. BUT AT LEAST I KNOW I CAN TRUST YOU.

I'D LOVE TO FUCKING KNOW HOW YOU WORK THAT ONE OUT...

ON THE PHONE YOU TOLD ME YOU GUARANTEED MY SAFETY. DOES THAT STILL HOLD TRUE?

IF THIS IS 'COS OF WHAT YOU SAID THE LAST TIME, WHERE YOU THINK I'M READY TO JUMP SHIP--

JUST TELL ME--DOES IT STILL HOLD TRUE?

IT DOES UNTIL I DROP YOU OFF.

ONCE THE BOSS HAS YOU, THAT'S MY PART OF IT OVER. THAT'S WHEN YOU'RE ON YOUR OWN.

THAT'S ALL I ASK.

... FUCKING WEIRD.

WHERE ARE WE GOING?

SOME M.O.D. PLACE OUTSIDE LONDON. THEY KNOW ABOUT TREATING SUPERHUMAN CASUALTIES, APPARENTLY.

WHY DID YOU JOIN THE S.A.S., HAWKINS?

WHAT THE FUCK DO YOU CARE?

EVERYONE IN SPECIAL FORCES HAS THEIR REASONS. I'M JUST WONDERING WHAT YOURS WERE.

AH, IT'S A LONG STORY...

THE ALTERNATIVE IS SEVEN HUNDRED AND FIFTY GAMES OF I-SPY.

WELL... FUCK IT, WHY NOT?

ALL RIGHT, LET'S SEE. YOU EVER BEEN TO A PLACE CALLED LUTON?

NO...

"DON'T."

UH! UH! UH! UH!

KEV, IS IT IN YET?

'ERE, DID I TELL YA ME UNCLE DON KILLED 'IMSELF?

UH! UH! UH! UH! UH!

SAID 'E COULDN'T STAND IT ANYMORE. 'E'D LIVED 'ERE FIFTY YEARS AN' ANYFING WAS BETTER'N ISS...

UH! UH! UH! UH!

I DUNNO WHAT 'E MEANT, MESELF. I FINK LUTON'S TRIFFIC.

UUNNNHH!

AW, FACKSAKE, YA MADE ME DROP ME FACKIN' KEBAB!

STUPID WANKA! RIGHT, YA CAN BLOODY BUY ME ANNUVAH ONE, 'EN!

WOT?!

ONLY HAD ENOUGH FOR-- FOR ONE--

FACKIN' CAHNT!

?

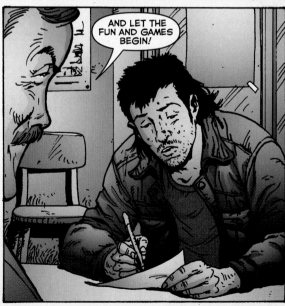

PRETTY INSPIRING SO FAR.

AH, IT WAS ALL RIGHT. I MEAN ULSTER WAS SHIT, BUT I ENDED UP REALLY LIKING THE ARMY. I WAS GOOD AT A LOT OF THE STUFF.

AND I LIKED HAVING MY MATES 'ROUND ME, I LIKED BEING PART OF SOMETHING...

HERE, TONE? WHO'RE THOSE TWO LADS OVER THERE?

EH?

I KEEP SEEIN' THEM ABOUT THE PLACE, THEY JUST COME AN' GO AS THEY PLEASE. THEY DON'T SALUTE THE OFFICERS, THEY WEAR WHATEVER THEY WANT--IT'S LIKE NOBODY FUCKIN' DARES GO NEAR THEM...

THOSE TWO? THEY'RE FROM THE REGIMENT, MATE.

THE REG... WHAT, THE S.A.S.?

YEAH. THEY DO ALL THIS UNDERCOVER STUFF 'ROUND THE CITY.

I THOUGHT THEY'D BE HARD AS FUCKIN' NAILS...

THEY ARE, KEV.

BUT THEY'VE GOT FUCK ALL TO PROVE TO ANYONE.

I DIDN'T THINK ANYTHING MORE ABOUT IT AT THE TIME, BUT I KNOW I LIKED THE IDEA. JUST GETTING ON WITH THE JOB, NONE OF THAT ARMY DISCIPLINE BOLLOCKS.

ANYWAY, THE OTHER GREAT THING ABOUT BEING A SQUADDIE IS THE WAY BIRDS GO MAD FOR THE UNIFORM...

"SO ONE NIGHT WHEN THE BATTALION'S BACK IN BLIGHTY, I MANAGE TO COP OFF WITH THIS BIG BIT OF POSH..."

BLOODY-- HELL-- !

THAT'S IT! THAT'S IT! OOOOH, YOU LOVELY BOY!

AND TROT! FASTER NOW! FASTER! AND CANTER!

AND GALLOP! YES! OH YES! OH YES-YES-YES-YES--

WHAT THE BLOODY HELL IS GOING ON HERE?!

MARJORIE! YOU APPALLING SLUT!

OH, WHAT A FRIGHTFUL BORE...!

YOU! GET YOUR HANDS OFF MY WIFE THIS INSTANT, YOU DISGUSTING LITTLE SWINE!

...I GO AWAY FOR TWO DAYS AND ALREADY YOU'RE BRINGING SOME GHASTLY OIK HOME! I WON'T BLOODY WELL STAND FOR IT, MARJORIE! I TOLD YOU THAT THE LAST TIME!

DO PIPE DOWN, DEREK. YOU TOLD ME THAT THE LAST *NINE* TIMES, AND YOU DON'T SEEM TO HAVE LEFT YET...

JESUS...

GET OUT! YOU FILTHY, GRUBBY LITTLE COMMONER, GET OUT OF MY HOUSE AT ONCE!

WELL THAT'S WHAT I'M FUCKING DOING--!

HOW DARE YOU! I'LL THRASH YOU WITHIN AN INCH OF YOUR LIFE!

MATE: BEHAVE YOURSELF.

"BIG FUCKING DEAL, RIGHT? WELL, ABOUT SIX MONTHS LATER OUR C.O. GETS PROMOTED TO BRIGADIER AND THE WHOLE LOT OF US ARE PARADED FOR THE NEW BLOKE..."

GET A HAIRCUT.

STRAIGHTEN YOUR BERET.

THAT MOUSTACHE IS *NOT* REGULATION...

OH MY GOD.

AND WHAT IS YOUR NAME, LANCE-CORPORAL?

HAWKINS, SIR!

NO. OH NO.

YOUR NAME IS PRIVATE SHIT.

"IT WAS THE START OF THE WORST SIX MONTHS OF MY LIFE.

"EVERY SHIT FUCKING DETAIL GOING, EVERY BOLLOCKS CHARGE HE COULD GET ME ON--I GOT THE LOT.

"I WAS FLAPPING GOOD STYLE--EVEN THOUGHT ABOUT LEAVING THE ARMY. WHICH WOULD HAVE BEEN FUCKING CRAP, IT WAS THE LAST THING I WANTED TO DO.

"I STILL HATED THE BULLSHIT, BUT THE REST OF IT WAS A SCREAM. I WAS TWENTY YEARS OLD AND I'D BEEN ALL OVER THE WORLD--AND NOW IT WAS ALL FUCKED, JUST 'CAUSE THIS CUNT CAUGHT ME UP TO ME NUTS IN HIS OLD SLAPPER'S GUTS.

"I MEAN WHAT THE HELL WAS I GONNA DO? FUCKING GO BACK TO LUTON?

HIS FAVORITE ONE, RIGHT, WAS ALWAYS HAVING ME ON THE RANGE FOR GRENADE PRACTICE. LOT OF L-2s DON'T GO OFF--SO SOME POOR FUCKER HAS TO CRAWL UP TO THE DUDS AND TIE A BIT OF DET CORD 'ROUND THEM, THEN SET THEM OFF THAT WAY.

GUESS WHO?

JEEEEZUSS CHRRIIIIIST...!

"IT WAS 'ROUND ABOUT THEN I HAD A BIT OF A BRAINWAVE."

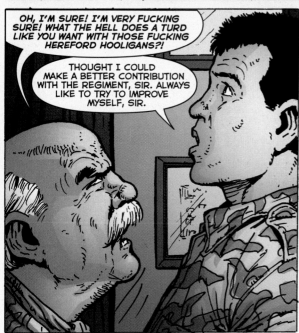

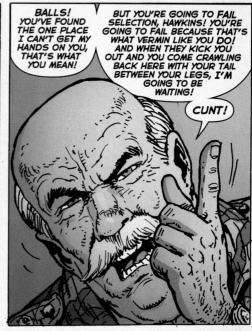

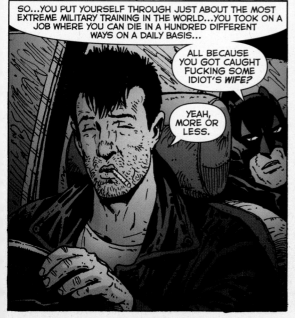

WELL?!

ALL RIGHT, TAKE IT EASY...

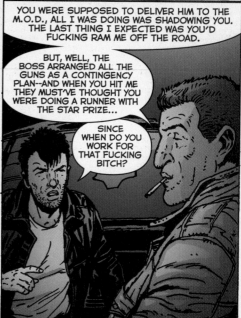

YOU WERE SUPPOSED TO DELIVER HIM TO THE M.O.D., ALL I WAS DOING WAS SHADOWING YOU. THE LAST THING I EXPECTED WAS YOU'D FUCKING RAM ME OFF THE ROAD.

BUT, WELL, THE BOSS ARRANGED ALL THE GUNS AS A CONTINGENCY PLAN--AND WHEN YOU HIT ME THEY MUST'VE THOUGHT YOU WERE DOING A RUNNER WITH THE STAR PRIZE...

SINCE WHEN DO YOU WORK FOR THAT FUCKING BITCH?

MICK...

HOW LONG HAVE YOU BEEN OUT OF THE REGIMENT...?

ABOUT SIX MONTHS OR SO. THE COLONEL WAS IN ON IT.

THEY MADE ME A FUCKING GOOD OFFER, KEV. THEY SET EVERYTHING UP, ALL I HAD TO DO WAS STAY IN HEREFORD AS IF I WAS STILL WITH B SQUADRON, AND JUST SORT OF... KEEP AN EYE ON THINGS...

THINGS LIKE ME?

SHE DOESN'T SEEM TO TRUST YOU TOO MUCH, MATE.

COME ON, KEV, YOU KNOW IT'S NOTHING PERSONAL. I'M DOING A FUCKING JOB, JUST LIKE YOU ARE.

WHO CARES WHO WINS, ISN'T THAT WHAT WE USED TO SAY? 'COS WE JUST LIKED DOING THE WORK, WE DIDN'T GIVE A SHIT WHO WAS SUPPOSED TO BE RIGHT OR WRONG?

Next: *Days of Kevin*

...WAS INFORMED THAT FATHER HARRINGTON HAD FORCED HIS THIRTEEN YEAR-OLD LOVER TO HAVE AN ABORTION...

SO FAR THE VATICAN HAS MADE NO OFFICIAL COMMENT, BUT AT A MAJOR ECCLESIASTICAL BUNFIGHT IN ROME TODAY THE POPE HIMSELF WAS HEARD TO REMARK, "GOTT IN HIMMEL! DONNERWETTER! ACHTUNG, ACHTUNG, ENGLANDER TERRORFLEIGER!"

IN OTHER NEWS, THE NORTHERN IRELAND PEACE PROCESS HAS RUN INTO TROUBLE ONCE AGAIN...

A DEMOCRATIC UNIONIST PARTY SPOKESMAN ACCUSED THE PROVISIONAL I.R.A. OF PREVARICATING ON ITS PROMISE TO FIND A FORM OF WORDS TO ACCURATELY DESCRIBE A METHOD OF PUTTING ITS WEAPONS BEYOND USE. A SPOKESMAN FOR SINN FEIN, THE I.R.A.'S POLITICAL WING, SAID THAT REPUBLICANS WOULD NOT BE DRAWN INTO WHAT HE CALLED THE POLITICS OF SCRABBLE...

OH, YOU CUNTS.

DON'T FUCK IT UP NOW.

NOT AFTER ALL THAT FUCKING SHIT...

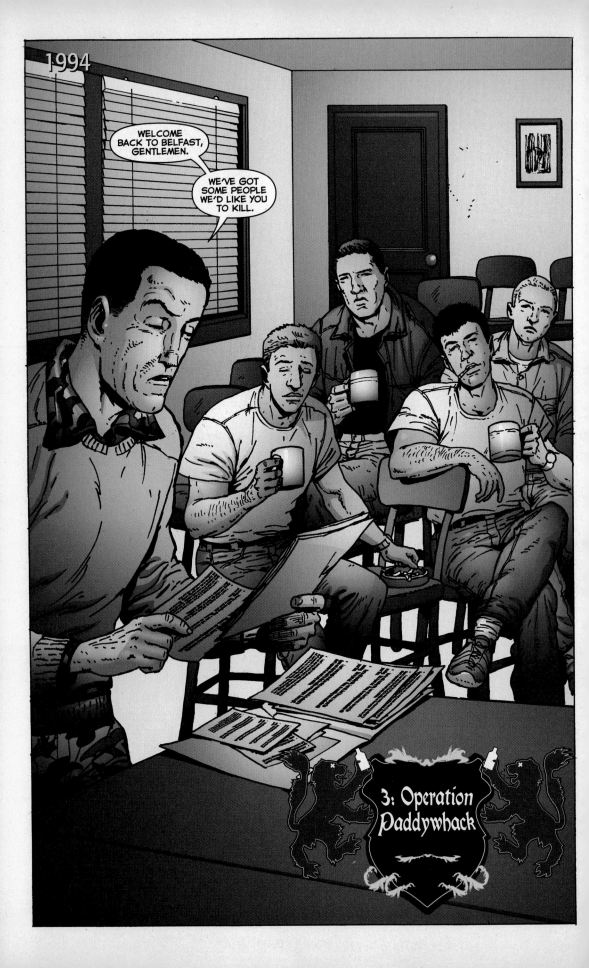

AS YOU KNOW, *PIRA* HAVE BEEN ON THE VERGE OF CALLING A CEASEFIRE FOR SOME TIME NOW. ONCE THEY DO, LOYALIST PARAMILITARIES LIKE THE U.V.F. AND U.F.F. ARE EXPECTED TO FOLLOW SUIT.

THE PROBLEM, OF COURSE, IS THAT A NUMBER OF KEY PLAYERS ON BOTH SIDES REFUSE TO COUNTENANCE WHAT THEY SEE AS AN OUTRIGHT SURRENDER--NOTHING LESS THAN TOTAL VICTORY, YOU KNOW THE SORT OF THING. AND THAT'S WHERE YOU COME IN.

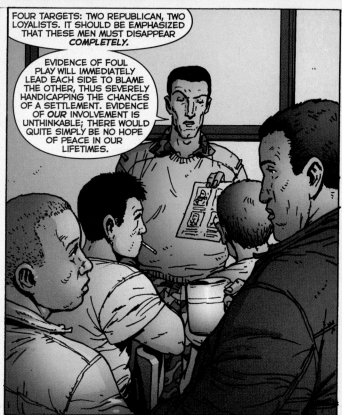

FOUR TARGETS: TWO REPUBLICAN, TWO LOYALISTS. IT SHOULD BE EMPHASIZED THAT THESE MEN MUST DISAPPEAR *COMPLETELY.*

EVIDENCE OF FOUL PLAY WILL IMMEDIATELY LEAD EACH SIDE TO BLAME THE OTHER, THUS SEVERELY HANDICAPPING THE CHANCES OF A SETTLEMENT. EVIDENCE OF *OUR* INVOLVEMENT IS UNTHINKABLE; THERE WOULD QUITE SIMPLY BE NO HOPE OF PEACE IN OUR LIFETIMES.

BOB, YOU'RE GOING TO RUN THIS ONE. KEV, NOW THAT YOU'VE GOT THAT STRIPE YOU MAY AS WELL GET USED TO THE LOFTY HEIGHTS OF COMMAND. YOU'RE 2 I/C.

FUCKING WONDERFUL...

YEAH, YEAH.

WE'VE GOT EXCELLENT INTEL, WITH PRECISE LOCATIONS FOR ALL OF THE TARGETS OVER THE COMING WEEK. HOW YOU ACTUALLY DO THE JOB IS UP TO YOU; WE KNOW THE FOUR OF YOU WORK WELL TOGETHER.

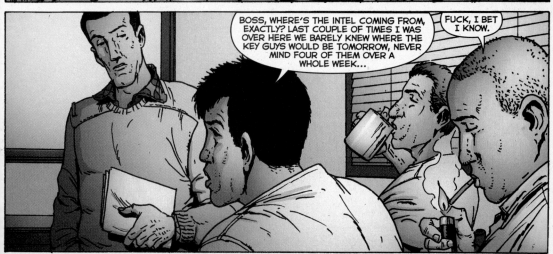

BOSS, WHERE'S THE INTEL COMING FROM, EXACTLY? LAST COUPLE OF TIMES I WAS OVER HERE WE BARELY KNEW WHERE THE KEY GUYS WOULD BE TOMORROW, NEVER MIND FOUR OF THEM OVER A WHOLE WEEK...

FUCK, I BET I KNOW.

I'M ALL EARS.

IT'S THEIR OWN PEOPLE, MATE.

PIRA ARMY COUNCIL CAN'T JUST SEND ITS LADS OUT TO SLOT THEIR MATES, ANY MORE THAN THE OPPOSITION CAN. BUT LET'S SAY THERE'S AN UNFORTUNATE SECURITY LEAK, AND SOMEHOW THE BRITS FIND OUT WHERE THE TROUBLEMAKERS ARE...

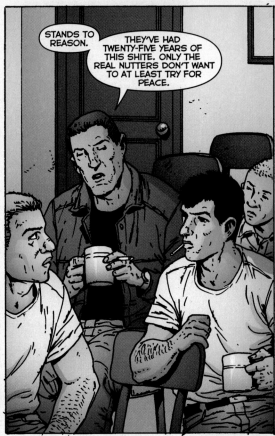

STANDS TO REASON.

THEY'VE HAD TWENTY-FIVE YEARS OF THIS SHITE. ONLY THE REAL NUTTERS DON'T WANT TO AT LEAST TRY FOR PEACE.

WHEN YOU PUT IT LIKE THAT...

WHO GIVES A SHIT, ANYWAY? LET'S JUST GET ON WITH THE FUCKING JOB.

STIRRING WORDS, MICK. EXACTLY THE CALL TO ARMS I WAS GOING TO OFFER.

LET ME JUST MAKE TWO FINAL POINTS...

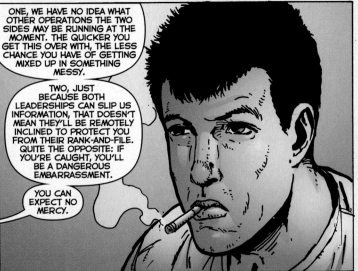

ONE, WE HAVE NO IDEA WHAT OTHER OPERATIONS THE TWO SIDES MAY BE RUNNING AT THE MOMENT. THE QUICKER YOU GET THIS OVER WITH, THE LESS CHANCE YOU HAVE OF GETTING MIXED UP IN SOMETHING MESSY.

TWO, JUST BECAUSE BOTH LEADERSHIPS CAN SLIP US INFORMATION, THAT DOESN'T MEAN THEY'LL BE REMOTELY INCLINED TO PROTECT YOU FROM THEIR RANK-AND-FILE. QUITE THE OPPOSITE: IF YOU'RE CAUGHT, YOU'LL BE A DANGEROUS EMBARRASSMENT.

YOU CAN EXPECT NO MERCY.

AS IF ANYONE'D EXPECT MERCY FROM THE PADDIES...

YOU KNOW THE RUPERTS, KEV. THEY LOVE A LITTLE TOUCH OF DRAMA.

RIGHT, WHO'S DOING WHAT: MICK, WEAPONS AND VEHICLES. THIS HAS TO BE A HUNDRED PER CENT DENIABLE, SO BEAR THAT IN MIND WHEN YOU'RE SORTING ALL THE SHIT OUT.

SUPPRESSED PISTOLS, FOR STARTERS. TWO CARS?

THEY'LL PING US STRAIGHTAWAY WITH JUST THE ONE.

TINY, YOU'RE ON THE SCALEY KIT. IF IT TURNS INTO A GANGFUCK, WE'LL NEED THE GREEN ARMY TO COME AND GET US OUT.

WE'RE *YANKEE ONE-ZERO*, IT SAYS HERE. THEY'LL BE LISTENING OUT FOR US.

HERE, YOU'RE THE LOCAL EXPERT. SEE IF YOU CAN WORK OUT THE BEST TIMES AND PLACES TO SLOT THESE CUNTS.

AND DON'T FORGET WE'VE GOT TO TAKE 'EM WITH US; SOMEONE'S GOING TO BE KICKING 'EM OUT OF A CHINOOK OVER THE IRISH SEA TOMORROW...

WHAT ABOUT YOU?

I'M OFF FOR A WANK, MATE.

HAVE FUN.

GOOD ONE?

YEAH, I THOUGHT ABOUT KEV'S MUM.

S'POSE IT MAKES A CHANGE FROM YOURS.

RIGHT, WE'RE AGREED THE BEST WAY IS TO DO THE WHOLE THING IN ONE NIGHT. THE LONGER WE'RE HERE, THE DODGIER IT GETS.

"THURSDAY HAS THE FOUR OF THEM CLOSER TO EACH OTHER THAN AT ANY OTHER TIME.

"TOMMY CURRIE'S GONNA BE AT HIS GIRLFRIEND'S HOUSE IN TURF LODGE. SAM BRIDGES'LL BE COMING HOME FROM THE PUB--DRUNK OFF HIS ARSE--UP AT THE TOP OF THE SHANKILL. JOE FARRELL SHOULD BE AT HOME TOO, JUST OFF THE CRUMLIN ROAD.

"THE ONE PROBLEM IS STEVIE WHITE, ALL THE WAY OVER IN SYDENHAM. WE'LL HAVE TO DO HIM LAST."

"FAIR ENOUGH, KEV. ALL RIGHT, TWO TEAMS: YOU AND MICK AND ME AND TINY.

"WE'LL TAKE IT IN TURNS: ONE LOT DOES THE JOB, THE OTHER COVERS. THAT SEEM FAIR ENOUGH?"

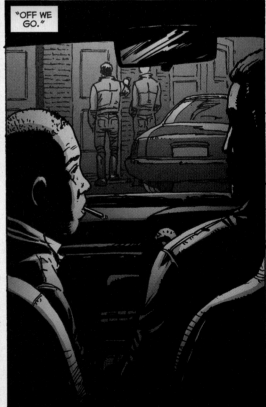

"OFF WE GO."

WHUH?

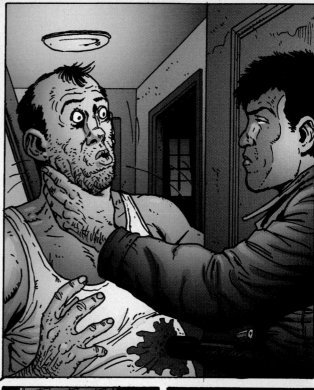

TOMMY...?

TOMMY, ARE YE COMIN' BACK TO BED?

IT'S ALL RIGHT, SO IT IS. IT CAN HAPPEN TO ANYONE.

WE CAN TRY AGAIN IN A COUPLA MINUTES...

GGGRrrrrrr

GGGRrrrrrrrr

GRRAAAARRR!

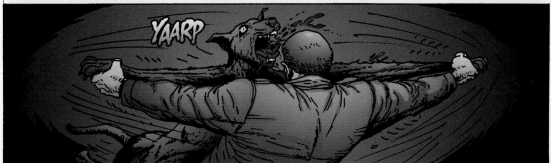

YAARP

WHAT...?

FUCK!

NO CLEAR SHOT!

ON 'EM!

JESUS--!

AAAAAAHH!

LAST ONE LEGGED IT! FRONT DOOR'S SECURE!

IT'S GONE NOISY...

WE NEED TO KNOW HOW MUCH SHIT WE'RE IN.

SO WHAT WAS ALL THAT ABOUT, CUNT?

YE'LL NOT MAKE ME TALK, YE FUCKIN' BRIT BASTARD!

NO?

FUCKIN' RIGHT Y--

WAAAAH!

BIG BOYS' RULES, MATE. WHAT ABOUT YOU, CAN I MAKE YOU TALK?

Y-Y-Y-Y-YES--!

THEY WERE HIS PEOPLE, THEY WERE A FUCKIN' PROVIE DEATH SQUAD! THEY FOUND OUT ME AN' HIM WERE DOIN' BUSINESS!

YEAH?

AYE, WE WERE FLOGGIN' TAPES, YE KNOW? WE STARTED OUT WI' A BITTA DOPE, BUT WE MADE A FUCKIN' FORTUNE WI' THE FILMS...

FILMS?

WELL...DIRTY ONES, LIKE.

WE MET UP IN PRISON, WE THOUGHT HE COULD SELL IN HIS PART A TOWN AN' I COULD SELL IN MINE.

VERY FUCKING INSPIRING. NICE TO KNOW THERE'S HOPE FOR PEACE AFTER ALL.

SO PIRA FOUND OUT AND SENT THESE BOYS TO SLOT YOU?

NO, NO, IT'S NOT THE BIG BOYS! IT'S JUST THE ONES WERE CLOSEST TO HIM, ALL THEY WANT'S THE MONEY!

THEY LIFTED ME IN THE CITY CENTER THIS MORNIN', THEY WERE GONNA BEAT US TILL WE TOLD THEM WHERE THE CASH WAS...

TROUBLE.

BOY WHO GOT OUT'S COME BACK WITH SOME OF THE LOCALS. ALREADY A DOZEN OUT THE FRONT.

OH JESUS, THEY'LL KNOW WHO I AM! THEY'LL TEAR ME TO FUCKIN' PIECES!

THEY'RE NOT GONNA...

THEY ARE, YOU KNOW.

Nooooooooo!

I THINK I'D QUITE LIKE TO GO HOME NOW.

STILL NO ALPHA.

WHAT THE FUCK'RE THEY PLAYING AT? FRONT DOOR, KEV--

WHY DON'T WE JUST BURN THE FUCKING HOUSE DOWN?

KEEP 'EM OCCUPIED WHILE WE GO OUT THROUGH THE ROOF.

HOW DO WE START A FIRE, THEN? FAST?

I MIGHT KNOW.

MICK, BOB, YOU STOP 'EM GETTING UP THE STAIRS. TINY, YOU'RE WITH ME.

AIMING A BIT HIGH, MICK.

SEE?

AAAAAH!

WHAT YOU LOOKING FOR?

NO GAS MAINS IN NORTHERN IRELAND. THEY TOOK 'EM OUT IN THE SEVENTIES, WHAT WITH THE BOMBS.

SO A LOT OF OLDER PLACES HAVE-- YES!

EH?

IT'S WHAT'S IN IT THAT COUNTS. GIVE US A HAND, WILL YOU?

THE CARS CAN BE DISCREETLY RECOVERED TOMORROW, THE BODIES DISPOSED OF AS PER THE ORIGINAL PLAN. THE FIRE WILL TAKE CARE OF ANY EVIDENCE YOU LEFT AT THE HOUSE.

THERE *IS* STILL THE QUESTION OF WHAT THE SURVIVOR OF THE INITIAL CONTACT AT THE HOUSE MIGHT HAVE TO SAY--

BUT I DOUBT THAT EITHER PIRA *OR* THE U.V.F. WILL BE KEEN TO PUBLICIZE THEIR ACCIDENTAL COLLUSION IN THE DISTRIBUTION OF HARDCORE PORNOGRAPHY.

WELL DONE, GENTLEMEN. I THINK WE CAN SAFELY SAY THAT YOU HAVE STRUCK AN IMPORTANT BLOW FOR PEACE.

WHAT THE FUCK HAPPENED TO OUR BACK-UP, SIR?

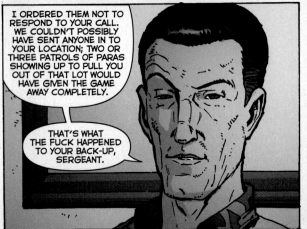

I ORDERED THEM NOT TO RESPOND TO YOUR CALL. WE COULDN'T POSSIBLY HAVE SENT ANYONE IN TO YOUR LOCATION; TWO OR THREE PATROLS OF PARAS SHOWING UP TO PULL YOU OUT OF THAT LOT WOULD HAVE GIVEN THE GAME AWAY COMPLETELY.

THAT'S WHAT THE FUCK HAPPENED TO YOUR BACK-UP, SERGEANT.

I SUGGEST THE FOUR OF YOU GET SOME SLEEP. YOU'LL BE RETURNING TO HEREFORD FIRST THING IN THE MORNING.

WELL, AS COVERT OPS GO, THAT WAS...

DEFINITELY ONE OF THEM...

THERE NEVER WAS ANY BACK-UP IN THE FIRST PLACE, WAS THERE?

NO.

HE ONLY SAID THERE WAS IN CASE WE GOT COLD FEET ABOUT GOING IN.

OH, WELL. ANOTHER DAY, ANOTHER FEW QUID.

ANOTHER FUCKING NIGHTMARE TO ADD TO THE HEADFUL I'VE ALREADY GOT, MORE LIKE.

YEAH.

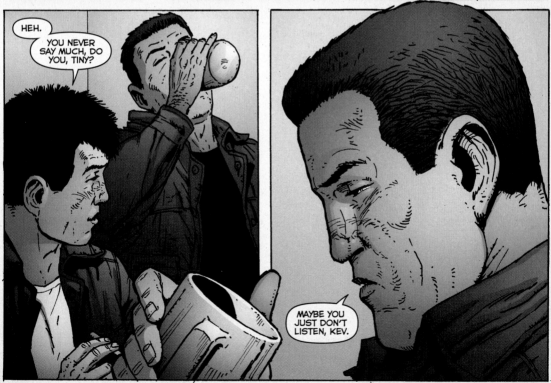

HEH.

YOU NEVER SAY MUCH, DO YOU, TINY?

MAYBE YOU JUST DON'T LISTEN, KEV.

THERE'S AN M.I.5 FILE CALLED *ROYAL OAK*, HAWKINS. THE PASSWORD IS *DANNY BOY*.

JESUS FUCK.

Next: Kevin Can Wait

YOU'RE WRONG.

YOU CAN DO ANYTHING YOU WANT IN THE WORLD, MATE. MAYBE ONE DAY YOU'LL REALIZE THAT.

"GOOD LUCK, KEV."

GIVE ME ANY SHIT AND I WILL FUCKING SHOOT YOU DEAD.

DO YOU UNDER-STAND?

K. JAMES

Y...Y...YES...!

THE MIDNIGHTER.

QUICK AS YOU LIKE.

SO WHO ARE THE NUTTERS DOWNSTAIRS?

IT--IT'S SORT OF COMPLICATED--!

I KNOW WHAT ROYAL OAK IS, IF THAT'S ANY HELP.

THEY'RE--WELL, THEY'RE THE FIRST COUPLE OF GROUPS WE TRIED WITH...THEY DIDN'T, UM, COME OUT TERRIBLY WELL...

WHY ARE THEY DRESSED UP LIKE ARSE-HOLES?

WE THOUGHT IT MIGHT, YOU KNOW, IT MIGHT SORT OF TRIGGER SOMETHING IN THEIR SUBCONSCIOUS...THEY COULD GRADUALLY BE TRAINED TO ADAPT THEIR BEHAVIOR TO FIT THEIR INTENDED PURPOSE...

DIDN'T WORK VERY WELL THOUGH, DID IT?

N-N-NO--!

WHICH IS WHY THAT SLAG IN WHITEHALL SIGNED THE JULY DIRECTIVE.

THAT'S GOT NOTHING TO DO WITH ME!

YEAH, RIGHT. I BET YOU WERE JUST ABOUT TO QUIT IN DISGUST AND GO TO THE PAPERS, WEREN'T YOU?

SWITCH THE LIGHT ON. I SEE ANYTHING OTHER THAN WHAT I'M EXPECTING AND I'LL BLOW YOUR LYING FUCKING HEAD OFF.

WELL, WELL.

YOU LOOK LIKE A RIGHT TWAT UP THERE, D'YOU KNOW THAT?

YES, I EXPECT I DO.

BUT I HAVEN'T MUCH EXPERIENCE AT IT.

OH, SHIT...!

WHAT THE FUCK ARE WE GONNA DO?

GET THEM OUT.

YEAH, BUT IT'S GONNA BE HARD ENOUGH GETTING YOU OUT OF HERE, I HADN'T PLANNED ON A LOAD OF KIDS...!

TOO BAD, THEY'RE COMING WITH US. I'VE ALREADY TOLD THEM SO.

YOU WHAT?

THEY'VE BEEN HERE SINCE YESTERDAY, I'VE BEEN TALKING TO THEM QUITE A BIT. I PROMISED I'D GET THEM OUT OF HERE AND TAKE THEM HOME.

WELL THAT'S-- FUCK!

YAAAH--!

BLOODY OUTRAGEOUS, IF YOU ASK ME.

LETTING THAT FUCKING POOF NEAR KIDS.

MICK--!

DIDN'T PING ME THIS TIME, DID YOU?

TAKE THE WEAPON OUT AND DROP IT IN THE SINK. WE BOTH KNOW THE DRILL, SO DON'T TRY AND BE A CUNT ABOUT IT.

HOW LONG...?

SINCE YESTERDAY IN THE PUB. FOLLOWED YOU ALL THE WAY HERE; I WAS FUCKING AMAZED WHEN I SAW YOU START CUTTING THE WIRE.

BACK-UP'LL BE HERE IN ABOUT TEN MINUTES. GO AND STAND NEXT TO YOUR MATE, THERE.

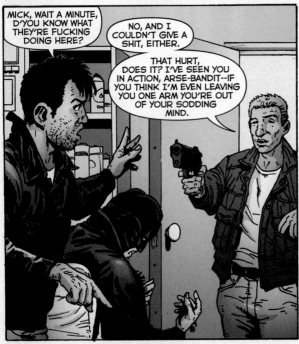

MICK, WAIT A MINUTE, D'YOU KNOW WHAT THEY'RE FUCKING DOING HERE?

NO, AND I COULDN'T GIVE A SHIT, EITHER.

THAT HURT, DOES IT? I'VE SEEN YOU IN ACTION, ARSE-BANDIT--IF YOU THINK I'M EVEN LEAVING YOU ONE ARM YOU'RE OUT OF YOUR SODDING MIND.

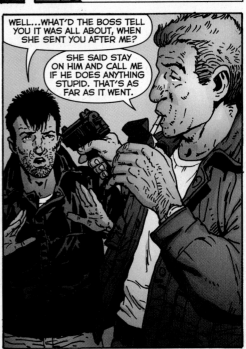

WELL...WHAT'D THE BOSS TELL YOU IT WAS ALL ABOUT, WHEN SHE SENT YOU AFTER ME?

SHE SAID STAY ON HIM AND CALL ME IF HE DOES ANYTHING STUPID. THAT'S AS FAR AS IT WENT.

HONESTLY, MATE.

I THINK YOU'RE GONNA WANT TO KNOW THIS.

OH YEAH?

ALL RIGHT...NINE YEARS AGO, OKAY? HIM AND APOLLO, YOU KNOW, THE OTHER ONE WE MET--

HIS BUMCHUM...

WELL, WHATEVER. THE TWO OF THEM HEARD ABOUT AN OPERATION BY A BLOKE CALLED *BENDIX*, WHO WAS THIS RIGHT FUCKING CUNT THEY USED TO KNOW.

AND WHAT THIS WAS, RIGHT, WAS EXPERIMENTS ON *KIDS*--LITTLE FUCKING KIDS, MICK, NO MORE THAN SEVEN OR EIGHT--TO TRY AND GIVE THEM *SUPERPOWERS*...

"SO THEY STEAM IN AND SLOT ALL THE BAD BOYS, EXCEPT THIS BENDIX WANKER, WHO ESCAPES, AND THEY'RE ON THEIR WAY OUT WHEN THEY RUN INTO TWO PLATOONS OF SQUADDIES..."

"BECAUSE THIS WAS *HERE*, RIGHT? THE FUCKERS HAD SET UP SHOP JUST OUTSIDE NOTTINGHAM, AND SOMEHOW M.I.5 HAD GOTTEN WIND OF THEM. THE MIDNIGHTER AND APOLLO GOT THERE FIRST, BUT OUR LADS WENT IN THE SAME NIGHT--

"AND GUESS WHO WAS RUNNING THE SHOW ON OUR SIDE...?

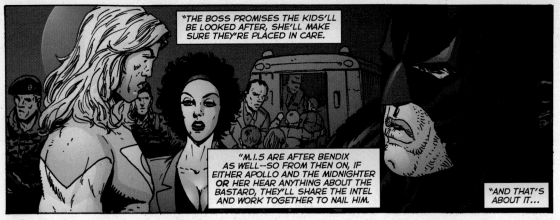

"THE BOSS PROMISES THE KIDS'LL BE LOOKED AFTER, SHE'LL MAKE SURE THEY'RE PLACED IN CARE.

"M.I.5 ARE AFTER BENDIX AS WELL--SO FROM THEN ON, IF EITHER APOLLO AND THE MIDNIGHTER OR HER HEAR ANYTHING ABOUT THE BASTARD, THEY'LL SHARE THE INTEL AND WORK TOGETHER TO NAIL HIM.

"AND THAT'S ABOUT IT...

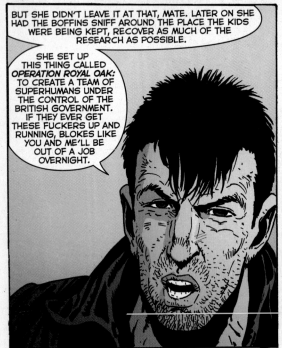

BUT SHE DIDN'T LEAVE IT AT THAT, MATE. LATER ON SHE HAD THE BOFFINS SNIFF AROUND THE PLACE THE KIDS WERE BEING KEPT, RECOVER AS MUCH OF THE RESEARCH AS POSSIBLE.

SHE SET UP THIS THING CALLED *OPERATION ROYAL OAK:* TO CREATE A TEAM OF SUPERHUMANS UNDER THE CONTROL OF THE BRITISH GOVERNMENT. IF THEY EVER GET THESE FUCKERS UP AND RUNNING, BLOKES LIKE YOU AND ME'LL BE OUT OF A JOB OVERNIGHT.

NOW, THE FIRST TIME THEY TRY IT, THE EXPERIMENT GOES A BIT PEAR-SHAPED. THE VOLUNTEERS END UP...SORT OF... *FUNNY...*

THAT THE FLIDS IN THAT ROOM YOU WERE LOOKING AT?

IT HAPPENS AGAIN, TOO. TAKES THEM AGES TO WORK OUT WHERE THEY'VE GONE WRONG.

"EVENTUALLY, AFTER YEARS OF PISSING ABOUT, THE EGGHEADS TELL THE BOSS THE SCORE: IT'S NOT THE PROCESS SO MUCH AS THE RAW MATERIAL.

"IF YOU WANT IT TO WORK, YOU HAVE TO DO WHAT BENDIX DID. YOU USE *CHILDREN,* NOT ADULTS--SOMETHING TO DO WITH, UH, IMMATURE PERSONALITIES COPING BETTER WITH BIO-ORGANIC ALTERATION, OR SOME BOLLOCKS LIKE THAT...

AND YOU NEED GENETIC MATERIAL FROM AN ACTUAL SUPERHUMAN.

BEATS TRYING TO GROW YOUR OWN, YOU SEE.

WHY HIM IN PARTICULAR?

ANY OF THE AUTHORITY WOULD HAVE DONE. EXCEPT THAT WALKING FUCKING USED TAMPON OF A DUTCHMAN, OBVIOUSLY.

I NEVER TRUSTED YOUR BOSS. APOLLO THOUGHT SHE'D BE A USEFUL CONTACT TO HAVE, BUT IF IT LOOKS LIKE A SNEAKY LITTLE CUNT THEN IT PROBABLY IS A SNEAKY LITTLE CUNT, THAT'S MY GENERAL RULE.

SO I KEPT TABS ON ROYAL OAK IN THE M.I.5 COMPUTER--NOT HARD TO DO WITH THE CARRIER'S TECHNOLOGY. I WASN'T TOO CONCERNED ABOUT THE SUPERHUMAN ENGINEERING; IT WAS OBVIOUS THEY WERE GOING NOWHERE WITH IT.

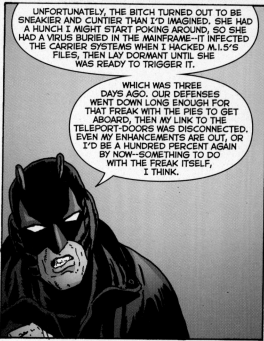

UNFORTUNATELY, THE BITCH TURNED OUT TO BE SNEAKIER AND CUNTIER THAN I'D IMAGINED. SHE HAD A HUNCH I MIGHT START POKING AROUND, SO SHE HAD A VIRUS BURIED IN THE MAINFRAME--IT INFECTED THE CARRIER SYSTEMS WHEN I HACKED M.I.5'S FILES, THEN LAY DORMANT UNTIL SHE WAS READY TO TRIGGER IT.

WHICH WAS THREE DAYS AGO. OUR DEFENSES WENT DOWN LONG ENOUGH FOR THAT FREAK WITH THE PIES TO GET ABOARD, THEN MY LINK TO THE TELEPORT-DOORS WAS DISCONNECTED. EVEN MY ENHANCEMENTS ARE OUT, OR I'D BE A HUNDRED PERCENT AGAIN BY NOW--SOMETHING TO DO WITH THE FREAK ITSELF, I THINK.

WHAT I DIDN'T KNOW AT THE TIME--WHAT I KNOW NOW, BECAUSE THE BITCH CAME HERE HERSELF AND QUITE OBVIOUSLY GOT WET TELLING ME--WAS THAT IN JULY SHE SIGNED AN ORDER AUTHORIZING SIX CHILDREN TO BE TRANSFERRED FROM A STATE-RUN ORPHANAGE. SHE CHOSE KIDS WITH BEHAVIORAL PROBLEMS SO IT WOULD LOOK LIKE THEY WERE BEING MOVED INTO SPECIALIST CARE.

THEN SHE TRIGGERED THE VIRUS ON THE CARRIER--

AND NOW SHE HAS EVERYTHING SHE NEEDS.

BEATS ME WHY SHE DIDN'T JUST HAVE YOU ZAPPED STRAIGHT HERE...

SHE TRIED, BUT HER CONTROL OF THE CARRIER WAS STILL ONLY PARTIAL WHEN I OPENED THE DOOR. THE CO-ORDINATES WERE SCRAMBLED; I ENDED UP THREE HUNDRED MILES NORTH OF WHERE SHE WANTED ME.

BUT IF I WERE YOU, HAWKINS?

I'D BE MORE CONCERNED WITH THE EFFECT THESE EARTH-SHATTERING REVELATIONS HAVE HAD ON YOUR FRIEND HERE.

BECAUSE FROM WHERE I'M SITTING, IT LOOKS LIKE SWEET FUCK ALL.

MICK...THESE ARE *KIDS* WE'RE TALKING ABOUT...

I MEAN THEY'RE GONNA EXPERIMENT ON THEM, THEY COULD EVEN END UP *KILLING* THEM...

WHAT, THERE'S NOT ENOUGH PEOPLE IN THE WORLD, OR SOMETHING?

NO. NO, YOU'RE *NOT* GONNA FUCKING DO THIS...!

I DUNNO HOW MANY TIMES I CAN TELL YOU THIS, KEV. I'M DOING A FUCKING JOB.

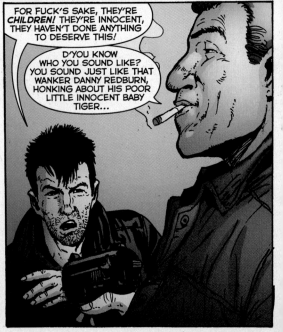

FOR FUCK'S SAKE, THEY'RE *CHILDREN!* THEY'RE INNOCENT, THEY HAVEN'T DONE ANYTHING TO DESERVE THIS!

D'YOU KNOW WHO YOU SOUND LIKE? YOU SOUND JUST LIKE THAT WANKER DANNY REDBURN, HONKING ABOUT HIS POOR LITTLE INNOCENT BABY TIGER...

DANNY HAD THE RIGHT IDEA, YOU ARSEHOLE! HE TOOK HIS TIGER AND HE GOT THE FUCK OUT OF THIS BOLLOCKS!

WHAT, YOU MEAN THE REGIMENT?

I MEAN THIS *HORRIBLE FUCKING LIFE WE LIVE,* WHERE YOU END UP DEAD OR FUCKED OR MENTAL! THAT'S WHAT I FUCKING MEAN, *MICK!*

KEV, IF IT'S SUCH A NIGHTMARE FOR YOU, WHY DIDN'T YOU JUST DO A RUNNER TOO?

OR SLOT YOURSELF, LIKE THAT FUCKING IDIOT TINY...

TINY... TINY WAS YOUR *MATE...*

HE WAS A PATHETIC CUNT.

FOR CHRIST'S SAKE, HAWKINS--!

HE'S ONLY USING KUNG FU! DIDN'T THEY EVEN TEACH YOU KUNG FU?

COME ON, AT LEAST KEEP YOUR GUARD UP! BLOCK HIM!

OH, THIS IS LAMENTABLE...!

ALWAYS KNEW YOU'D BE SOFT AS SHITE IF IT EVER CAME TO IT, KEV.

OH, GROW UP, D'YOU HONESTLY THINK I'M WORRIED ABOUT *HIM?* THUGS LIKE HIM ARE TEN-A-PENNY, YOU OUGHT TO KNOW THAT IF ANYONE DOES.

I'M REFERRING TO YOUR INSUBORDINATION AND DISOBEDIENCE. I'M SUGGESTING THAT YOU REMEMBER *WHICH SIDE YOU ARE ON.*

SO HOW...?

YOU APPEAR TO BE HOLDING A LOADED WEAPON.

HINT-HINT...

BUT--

GENETIC MATERIAL IS JUST AS EASY TO HARVEST AFTER DEATH. THE MIDNIGHTER WILL SERVE AS A REASONABLY APT DEMONSTRATION OF YOUR GOOD FAITH.

AFTER ALL, WHAT'S THE ALTERNATIVE? LIVE THE REST OF YOUR LIFE AS A FUGITIVE?

LET'S FACE IT, HAWKINS, YOU'RE NOT A PARTICULARLY COMPLEX INDIVIDUAL.

YOU WANT A ROOF OVER YOUR HEAD AND REGULAR ACCESS TO SEX AND ALCOHOL, AND A MONTHLY INCOME TO GUARANTEE ALL THREE.

SO.

I...UH... I...

NO!

WHAT ABOUT THE GOOD LADS THE REGIMENT USES UP AND THROWS ON THE SCRAPHEAD, OR ALL OUR MATES WE'VE SEEN DIE FOR NOTHING? AND WHAT ABOUT IF WE GET ORDERED TO DO SOMETHING *REALLY* HORRIBLE?

WHAT ARE YOU GOING TO DO WHEN THE HEAD-SHEDS TELL YOU TO SLOT A LOAD OF KIDS?

THEY'RE NOT GONNA MAKE US DO THAT...!

KEV, THEY CAN MAKE YOU DO FUCKING *ANYTHING.*

YOU NEVER SAY MUCH, DO YOU, TINY?

"MAYBE YOU JUST DON'T LISTEN, KEV."

CHRIST-ALL-BLOODY-MIGHTY.

WHAT HAVE I FUCKING *DONE*?

Next: Oooh, Kevin is a Place on Earth

WELL, *THAT'S* GOING TO BE A DIFFICULT ONE TO MASTURBATE OVER...
5: As Free As The Wind Blows

IF I HAD EVEN ONE LIMB WORKING I'D RIP YOUR UCKING-FAY HEAD OFF FOR THAT, HOLE-ASSAY!

BUT YOU *DON'T*, DO YOU, OCOLATE-CHAY ABBER-STAY? YOU KNOW AS WELL AS I DO I'M YOUR ONLY CHANCE OF GETTING OUT OF HERE ALIVE!

LET'S HEAR THE BIG UCKING-MOTHERFAY MASTER-PLAN, THEN...

I'M LOODY-BAY WORKING ON IT, BELIEVE ME!

ESUS-JAY RIST-CHAY, I'VE JUST KILLED THE *BOSS*... I'M GOING TO HAVE TO LEAVE THE ODDING-SAY COUNTRY...

LET'S NOT FORGET THE MORE IMMEDIATE PROBLEM OF THE TWO DOZEN HEAVILY-ARMED TROOPS WAITING FOR US OUTSIDE.

YEAH, WELL I'M NOT SLOTTING ANY OF OUR LADS. EVEN IF IT IS THE ANKY-WAY ROYAL LATRINES.

HERE.

WAIT A MINUTE.

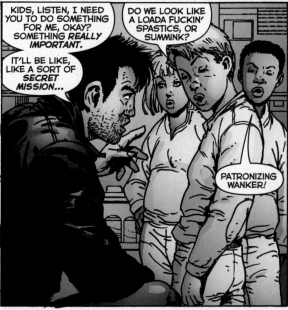

KIDS, LISTEN, I NEED YOU TO DO SOMETHING FOR ME, OKAY? SOMETHING *REALLY* IMPORTANT.

IT'LL BE LIKE, LIKE A SORT OF *SECRET* MISSION...

DO WE LOOK LIKE A LOADA FUCKIN' SPASTICS, OR SUMMINK?

PATRONIZING WANKER!

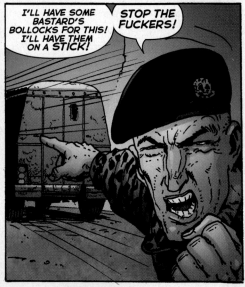

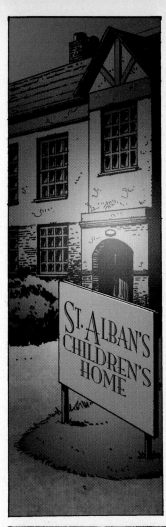

YOU WHAT?

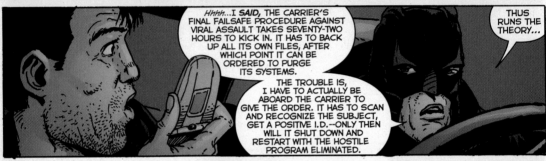

*Hhhh...*I **SAID**, THE CARRIER'S FINAL FAILSAFE PROCEDURE AGAINST VIRAL ASSAULT TAKES SEVENTY-TWO HOURS TO KICK IN. IT HAS TO BACK UP ALL ITS OWN FILES, AFTER WHICH POINT IT CAN BE ORDERED TO PURGE ITS SYSTEMS.

THE TROUBLE IS, I HAVE TO ACTUALLY BE ABOARD THE CARRIER TO GIVE THE ORDER. IT HAS TO SCAN AND RECOGNIZE THE SUBJECT, GET A POSITIVE I.D.--ONLY THEN WILL IT SHUT DOWN AND RESTART WITH THE HOSTILE PROGRAM ELIMINATED.

THUS RUNS THE THEORY...

SO YOU'RE GOING TO PHONE IT?

ONLY WAY WITH THE COMMS DOWN. HIT ONE SEVEN TIMES AND THEN THE STAR KEY; WE HAD TO MAKE SURE THE DOCTOR COULD REMEMBER IT.

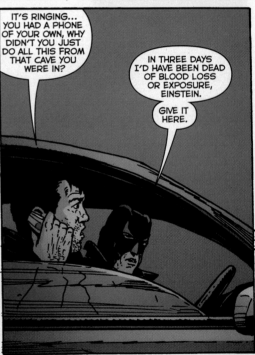

IT'S RINGING... YOU HAD A PHONE OF YOUR OWN, WHY DIDN'T YOU JUST DO ALL THIS FROM THAT CAVE YOU WERE IN?

IN THREE DAYS I'D HAVE BEEN DEAD OF BLOOD LOSS OR EXPOSURE, EINSTEIN.

GIVE IT HERE.

DOOR.

THE CARRIER

THE DEATH STAR CAN SUCK ITS BIG FAT COCK

BLOODY HELL...!

WHAT-- WHY AM I HERE? I DON'T WANT TO BE ON A SPACE STATION!

YOU'RE A WANTED MAN BACK HOME, HAWKINS. YOU KNOW THAT BITCH'LL HAVE LEFT A REPORT.

BUT--

I'M

SHUT UP!

I'M

IT'S THE THING.

OH, JESUS--

I'M

CARRIER! PURGE!

...A VAGINA...

FROGGETT?!

NOW THAT'S WHAT I CALL AN INCREDIBLY SMALL DICK.

Er... um...

H-H-HELLO, MATEY...

WHAT ARE YOU DOING HERE, YOU LITTLE NOB-END?

ACTUALLY--

CAN WE GO BACK A BIT FURTHER THAN THAT?

AND:

PIES...?

THANK GOD FOR THAT. WHEN I WOKE UP I THOUGHT I'D COME IN MY OWN FACE.

THE BOSS FORCED ME INTO IT, YOU KNOW. I'D NEVER HAVE WILLINGLY HARMED ANYONE, BUT--

BOLLOCKS...

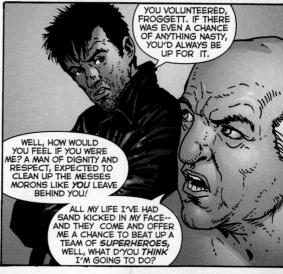

YOU VOLUNTEERED, FROGGETT. IF THERE WAS EVEN A CHANCE OF ANYTHING NASTY, YOU'D ALWAYS BE UP FOR IT.

WELL, HOW WOULD YOU FEEL IF YOU WERE ME? A MAN OF DIGNITY AND RESPECT, EXPECTED TO CLEAN UP THE MESSES MORONS LIKE *YOU* LEAVE BEHIND YOU!

ALL MY LIFE I'VE HAD SAND KICKED IN MY FACE-- AND THEY COME AND OFFER ME A CHANCE TO BEAT UP A TEAM OF *SUPERHEROES*, WELL, WHAT D'YOU *THINK* I'M GOING TO DO?

SO...

SO, ONCE THE BOSS'S VIRUS TOOK CONTROL OF THE CARRIER, SHE TELEPORTED ME ABOARD. I'D BEEN TRAINING FOR MONTHS, I KNEW HOW TO USE THE CARRIER'S OWN POWER TO CREATE AN *ILLUSIONARY CONSTRUCT* OF MYSELF--AND WITH THAT KIND OF ENERGY, I COULD BE AS BIG AND STRONG AS I WANTED.

AFTER THAT, MY JOB WAS EITHER TO NEUTRALIZE THE AUTHORITY, OR FLUSH AS MANY OF THE TEAM AS POSSIBLE DOWN TO EARTH...

I SUPPOSE YOU COULD LOOK LIKE WHATEVER YOU WANTED, TOO. WHICH REALLY DOES SAY IT ALL.

HEY!

WOULD YOU HAVE A ROOM WITH A DOOR I CAN LOCK, AND A BASEBALL BAT WITH A BIG FUCKING SPIKE IN THE END?

YOU KNOW-- I JUST MIGHT.

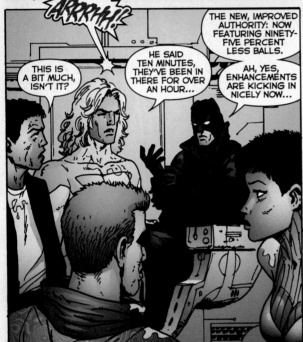

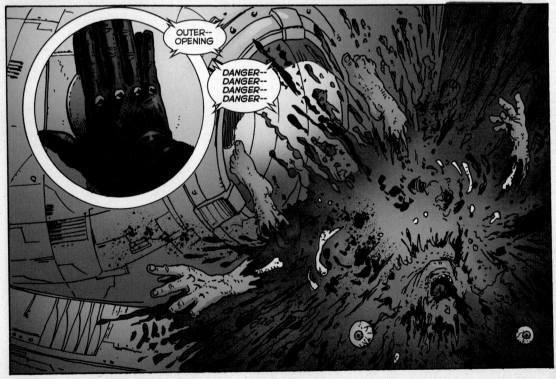

WHERE DO YOU WANT TO GO?

Hnnh. LONDON, I THINK.

KIND OF INTO THE LION'S DEN, ISN'T IT?

GOT SOME STUFF TO PICK UP, FEW THINGS I MIGHT BE NEEDING. AND I FANCY A LAST PINT BEFORE I START MY EXCITING NEW LIFE ON THE RUN.

RUNNING IS ONE WAY OF LOOKING AT IT.

ANOTHER IS THAT YOU'RE FINALLY FREE.

YEAH, WELL I'LL BE SURE TO REMEMBER HOW FREE I AM WHEN THE LADS FROM THE REGIMENT CATCH UP WITH ME ONE DARK NIGHT.

NEXT TIME ASK FOR SOME OTHER TOSSER, EH?

I'LL BE SURE TO. RELYING ON *YOU* TO SEE THE LIGHT WAS THE BIGGEST CRAPSHOOT OF MY ENTIRE LIFE.

UNLESS I'M A BETTER JUDGE OF CHARACTER THAN I GIVE MYSELF CREDIT FOR, WHICH I SERIOUSLY FUCKING DOUBT.

RIGHT THEN: OBVIOUSLY I'D RATHER EAT OUT RONALD REAGAN'S DEAD ASSHOLE THAN GET SENTIMENTAL AND SHAKE YOUR HAND, HAWKINS--BUT HERE'S SOMETHING THAT MIGHT COME IN USEFUL FOR A MAN KEEN TO STAY UNDERCOVER.

HELP YOU TO FLY UNDER THE RADAR, IF YOU SEE WHAT I MEAN.

WELL THAT'S, *Uh...* THAT'S...

YEAH, YEAH.

DOOR.

ARE YOU SURE YOU'RE FEELING ALL RIGHT?

BECAUSE GOING BY WHAT YOU SAID THE LAST TIME WE SAW HIM, I'M SURPRISED YOU DIDN'T JUST THROW HIM OUT THE AIRLOCK TOO...

THE THOUGHT DID CROSS MY MIND.

BUT SO DID ANOTHER ONE.

THERE ARE BILLIONS LIKE HIM DOWN THERE. AND THEY'LL TAKE A LONG, LONG TIME TO CHANGE THEIR WAYS.

MOST NEVER WILL.

SOMETHING TO THINK ABOUT, THE NEXT TIME WE SET OUT TO SAVE THE WORLD.

CHEERS, MATE.

WHERE THE FUCK DO I GO FROM HERE...

OH, YOU CUNT...

YOU FUCKING CUNT...!

ALL RIGHT, YOU BASTARD.

GOOD STITCH.

UH... 'SCUSE ME, MATE...

NO OFFENSE OR ANYTHING, BUT JUST SO YOU KNOW: YOU LOOK LIKE A BIT OF AN ARSEHOLE WEARING THAT IN HERE...

THAT'S ALL RIGHT, MATE. I *AM* A BIT OF AN ARSEHOLE.

OH. WELL.

I SUPPOSE THERE'S NO ANSWER TO THAT.

The End